FIT FOR THE GAME
SQUASH

Steven Seaton and Ian McKenzie

WARD LOCK

Text ©Ian McKenzie and Steven Seaton
©Ward Lock Limited 1991

Editor: Heather Thomas
Art Director: Rolando Ugolini
Produced by SP Design, St Andrews Castle,
33 St. Andrews St. South, Bury St. Edmunds.

Text set in Univers Medium by Halcyon Type & Design Ltd, Ipswich
Printed and bound in Great Britain by Richard Clay Ltd.

British Library Cataloguing in Publication Data

McKenzie, Ian
Squash.
1. Sports. Fitness.
I. Title.   II Series.
613711
ISBN 0-7063-6936-X

Steven Seaton

Steven Seaton first took up squash while closeted away in a Norfolk boarding school. Since those distant days he's continued his interest in the game on court as a regular club player whilst also pursuing a career as a sports journalist. He has written on a number of sports, specializing most recently in athletics and squash. He works as a staff writer on *Running Magazine* and *Squash Player Magazine* and edits the practical sections of both publications.

Ian McKenzie

Ian McKenzie is Consultant Editor of the authoritative *Squash Player Magazine* and is the author of a number of books on squash. A New Zealander, he lives in London and specializes in the coaching of international players.

Acknowledgements

The authors would like to thank Stripes Squash and Health Club, Ealing Broadway Centre, London, for the use of their facilities; Vicky Tarakjian and Damian Walker, for appearing in some of the photographs; and Dr Craig Sharp, chief physiologist at the British Olympic Medical Centre, for his advice.

All photographs are courtesy of Mark Shearman, with the exception of the cover and photographs on pages 6, 9, 10, 72 and 76, which were supplied by Stephen Line.

CONTENTS

FOREWORD

One of the coach's tasks is to assess players. It's a game we all like to play in sport, giving our opinion of players and teams, their capabilities, performance, condition and what they could do better. Assessment is not always so easy when we come to ourselves. Excuses are easier. Excuses like 'It wasn't my day.' 'I'm tired.' 'I was still thinking about work.' 'He was too fit.'

We could write pages of them that we have collected in changing rooms and bars. If we listed these excuses under their true meanings, the one category we know would come out on top is fitness. 'I'm not fit enough,' it would say 'I'm not sure what to do to get fit and I haven't put time aside to work on it.'

That's why we have written this book. So that excuses are no longer necessary. For those who are tired of excuses and losses, here is the means to do something about it.

As coaches and fitness consultants, we know of many players who aren't fit enough for their aspirations and because of this they will never reach their potential. We all see this in other players but it's time to recognize it in ourselves. Are you fit for the game?

If you are not and want to be, we trust that this book will be of great assistance. Good luck

Ian McKenzie and Steven Seaton

Australian Chris Dittmar, known as one of the strongest and most robust players on the professional circuit, also shows the flexibility needed to play the game.

INTRODUCTION

Squash is a fine work-out. There is the fun of the game and the thrill of competition while you take part in robust and varied exercise. It is a useful way to work on your fitness, but for the ambitious player the problem is not playing squash to get fit but getting fit to play squash, and then of getting fitter to play better squash.

Often players come off court a little dejected from defeat, but are able to rationalize it with the favourite old excuse, 'I'm not fit enough'. 'If only I was fitter,' the implication goes, 'then perhaps I would have won and certainly I could have played better.' Our purpose in this book is to help those players who are unhappy with the 'If only' excuse, to get into action.

You can improve your game by improving your fitness. It happens at club level and with champions. In 1966, in the British Open quarter-final at the Lansdowne Club in London, Jonah Barrington launched a spectacular career which took him to six British Open titles when his 'War of Attrition' defeated the superior skills, shots and tactics of the finest player of the day, Abou Taleb. In 1991 Jahangir Khan, unmotivated and out of condition, came back from a career in tatters to enter a strict regime of training that took him from podgy early season loser, to an unprecedented tenth British Open title.

However, improving your fitness does not require the superhuman efforts of a Barrington or Jahangir. A progressive balanced programme, sensibly timetabled and suitable for your lifestyle, aspirations and level of skill can give you that longed-for lift in standard. But before launching into copious fitness training it is important not to forget the development of your skills through solo and pairs practice and your tactics and temperament through match play. 'If only I was fitter,' should not be an obsession excluding improvement in other areas of your game.

There are three areas where fitness for squash is important. Firstly, you can get fit to play squash and use squash to maintain that fitness. The beginner or player returning to the game should progress gradually. Do *not* overdo it. If you have a history of poor health, heart problems or are over 35, it would be wise to have a medical checkup before playing and training. Next you can get fit to beat opponents who will not be quite as fit as you. Finally, you can build your fitness to a new level so that you can play and survive against better players and learn a new level of play.

Jahangir Khan made a spectacular comeback to the top of his form in 1991, winning his tenth British Open title after an unpromising beginning to the season. A strict regime of training put him back in peak condition for the game.

CHAPTER ONE

SQUASH & FITNESS

Jahangir Khan and Gamal Awad, the former World No. 2, hold the record for the longest competitive game ever played, at 2 hours 48 minutes. Geoff Hunt, the eight-times British Open winner, and Awad are reputed to have played a rally of over 400 shots lasting over 10 minutes. International games often last one and a half hours and occasionally go over two, whereas club games may last 45 minutes or more. Top international rallies average about 20 shots but there is a wide range of rally lengths varying from a few shots, to longer rallies of 40 or so and very long rallies of about a hundred. The higher the level of squash, the longer and harder the rallies.

Squash rallies are made up of fast bursts of movement. A player must have the stamina not only to survive hard rallies of variable length and intensity, but also to keep repeating this after the 10-second break (approximate) between rallies. The longer and more intense these bursts of movement are, the greater the fatigue and the more difficult the recovery. This fitness ability calls on various kinds of endurance and uses different energy systems. It is like the endurance required by a middle-distance runner.

The fast bursts of movement in squash involve a complex variety of movements – taking off, running, turning, twisting, lunging, jumping, braking, bracing and pushing back to the T. Not only are endurance and speed necessary for these fast varied movements, but muscular endurance is needed to repeatedly brake and recover. Strength is necessary to recover from difficult situations, and flexibility is important in allowing a player to stretch. Agility is required to maintain balance while all this is going on.

Fit players don't just survive rallies as they play; they maintain the consistency and accuracy of their shots, good movement and the ability to think tactically.

Fitness for squash then, involves a wide range of fitness abilities – we could call it multi-dimensional. This is why it is such a good work-out. The fit player must have at least satisfactory levels of fitness in each area, and those wanting to progress their game must work to overcome relative weaknesses. This chapter is to help you understand what is necessary for squash fitness. Later testing and assessments (perhaps taking advice from a professional coach) will allow you to understand what it is important to work on in your game. In the following chapters we look at the different constituent parts of fitness and see exactly what they involve.

Fitness for squash is multi-dimensional. Young England star Del Harris here demonstrates a combination of speed and agility.

Endurance

Endurance is a broad term that can refer to both short-term effort and long-term sustained activity. In squash, both types are required: long-term endurance to cope with work throughout a match, and short-term to deal with high energy bursts within the match.

Energy from sugars and fats is broken down in the digestive processes and is supplied to the muscles for work. This involves two different processes – the aerobic and anaerobic energy systems.

Aerobic endurance

Aerobic means 'with air', and aerobic endurance is muscular work done using oxygen. The greater the supply of oxygen, the longer the muscles will perform, and conversely the less oxygen the muscles receive, the quicker the build-up of waste products (such as lactic acid) and the more fatigued the muscles become.

Training the aerobic system is achieved by raising the heart rate to an appropriate level and keeping it there for an appropriate period of time. Appropriate levels vary depending on a player's state of training and age. For club-level players in their twenties, three half-hour sessions of train-ing each week, at a heart rate of around 150 beats per minute, will produce a good increase in aerobic fitness. Better players will have to work harder, which means increasing the frequency of the sessions as well as their length and severity.

A rough guide to an appropriate training level is to add 25 to the athlete's age and subtract that from 220 to give an approxi-mate training pulse to aim for. Thus for a 25-year-old the figure would be 170.

Aerobic training can use any form of physical activity, e.g. running, skipping, cycling, swimming etc., which lifts the pulse rate to the appropriate level.

Anaerobic endurance

Anaerobic means 'without air' and refers to the muscles' ability to work without oxygen. The anaerobic system is a short-term mechanism brought into action by the muscles when the aerobic system cannot cope. Energy is produced by two main anaerobic energy systems; the phospha-gen energy system and the lactic energy system.

For squash, the phosphagen system liberates phosphocreatine, which fuels the muscles for brief flurries of intense activity for 10, maybe even 20 seconds. The energy available from this system can be doubled through training.

The main anaerobic system, the lactic energy system, produces more energy than the aerobic system but with a penalty. At full power, glycolysis can proceed for only 30 or 40 seconds before the build-up of lactic acid brings the muscles to a virtual halt. This is felt as fairly severe fatigue.

Generally this system is trained using interval training methods (interval running, shuttles, ghosting) of about 45 seconds at maximum effort, with 45 seconds rest, twice a week. Keep the rests active and gradually build up to 10 or 12 sets of shut-tles. These are best performed at the end of a training session.

Rests allow time for accumulated lactic acid to diffuse out of the muscle into blood and for it to be cleared from the blood. When muscles stop working, their blood flow drops off very quickly – within about 20 seconds there is an appreciable drop in flow. This tends to lock up the lactic acid in the muscle, and this is why it is important to 'warm-down' after a hard work-out and use 'active rests' when interval training.

Local muscle endurance

This is the ability of the muscles to work over a long time and incorporates both the aerobic and anaerobic systems. In squash this involves primarily the legs and racket arm but also muscles of the back, stomach and shoulder used in braking, turning and stretching.

Strength

Squash players do not need strength in the same way as, say, a shotputter, but basic strength is still necessary in the legs, back, abdomen, shoulders, arm and wrist. Leg strength is crucial to brake, brace, and to push up and back from the most difficult shots. Grip strength is important so that the racket will not twist in the hand, and to allow the wrist to compensate for poor positions.

A simple moderate weights conditioning programme can be of benefit, especially if directed at the specific needs of the individual.

As well as helping to minimize injury problems, strength training can assist in the development of power and speed. (Power is the rate at which work is done.) Certain players will have particular weaknesses, such as lack of speed and agility or muscle atrophy due to injury which can be overcome by a specific strength-training programme.

Speed

Speed is a vital attribute in squash. In a contest between two evenly matched players there will be winners that cannot be reached by either player, but the quicker player will always get to more balls, make more successful returns, be able to apply more pressure and be the more likely winner, if his stamina lasts of course.

Speed is a general term used to describe quite different mechanisms which require different training approaches. We can talk about anticipation, which includes the ability to pick up cues on where to move; perceptual speed, the time it takes to respond; acceleration; whole body speed; speed and agility in movement as opposed to sprinting speed; and limb speed of hands and legs. Coaches can help analyse their pupils' individual requirements, and then design specific training programmes to bring about improvement.

Speed is the important component of power that moves the player fast into, and out of, the striking position. It is power and timing that imparts speed to the ball. Leg speed is gained by fast on-court shuttles, fast skipping and techniques such as plyometrics or depth-jumping.

Flexibility

Flexibility in squash allows a player a full range of movement; it does not restrict fluidity of movement and helps to prevent injury (pulled muscles).

Poor flexibility can result in 'muscle-boundness', stiff awkwardness in movement and a lack of suppleness and 'spring', causing poor performance and inefficient technique. It can also hinder speed and endurance qualities, as stiff muscles may have to work harder to overcome resistance. By increasing the possible range of movement, greater speed and agility may be achieved. Stretching should be an important part of your warm-up, warm-down and general training.

CHAPTER TWO

HOW FIT ARE YOU?

By now you should have a greater understanding of fitness and its importance to squash. Before you take the first steps towards improving it, you need to put your fitness to the test. Unfortunately squash is not the type of sport that lends itself to assessment solely by match performance. Other variants, technical, tactical or psychological, can have a greater influence on the final result. But quantifying the various components of fitness through off-court testing is important. It highlights areas of weakness, helps you to design an individual programme, measures your progress throughout the programme and provides the motivational targets necessary to maintain a demanding regime.

Sports physiology laboratories provide the most accurate tests but they are also the most expensive. A more widely available and cheaper option is a series of simple field tests. All the tests require a minimal amount of equipment and can be performed in a gym, on a squash court or at home. Remember, however, that such test results are highly individual and should be used only as comparisons to indicate progress or potential problems.

Endurance testing

Aerobic

Step test
For this you need a bench or a box (50cm/20 inches high for men; 45cm/18 inches for women; and 40cm/16 inches for children), a metronome and a stopwatch. Step up and down from the box to the rhythm of the metronome for a set time and record your pulse at the end. The number of steps per minute and the duration of the test can vary. A standard test is 30 steps a minute for five minutes, an easier one 20 steps for four minutes. Compare only tests that are the same length and have the same number of steps per minute.

At the end of the test, rest for one minute, then take your pulse for 30 seconds. If you could not keep pace with the metronome and had to stop early, note the time you stopped. Now you have two figures, your achieved stepping time in seconds and your pulse, put them in the equation below to calculate a rough fitness index.

$$\frac{\text{(achieved stepping time)} \times 100}{\text{(30-second pulse)} \times 5.5} = \text{Fitness index}$$

A higher score indicates greater fitness. As a guide, most club players should have an index of over 100 for the five-minute, 30-step test.

Opposite, each complete step has four separate movements equal to four beats of the metronome; 30 steps a minute therefore means 120 beats a minute. Maintain the same stepping rhythm and movement pattern throughout the test. At the top of each step, ensure that you stand upright and don't cheat.

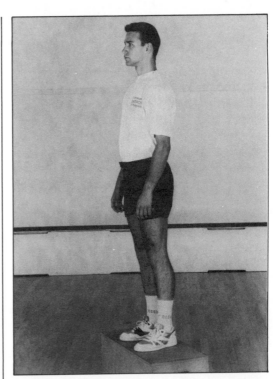

Pulse monitoring and running

Two simple alternative tests also gauge aerobic fitness. The first is simply to take a resting pulse for 30 seconds immediately after waking up in the morning. A rate around 40 indicates a good level of fitness; it will decrease as your cardio-respiratory capacity improves.

Another standard test, requiring nothing more than a stopwatch and a pair of running shoes, is the one-and-a-half-mile run. Complete the course as fast as possible; your time for the run is the test result. Once again, quicker times indicate progress.

Anaerobic

This is more difficult to measure in a non-laboratory test, but can be done with a series of diagonal shuttle runs on the court. Starting from the T, try to touch as many corners as possible with either your hand or racket in a set 30-40 second period. Ensure that you pass through the T every time, and maintain the same movement pattern in every test (for example, front right corner, front left corner, back right then back left). Repeat the test 4-6 times, resting no more than 15 seconds between tests.

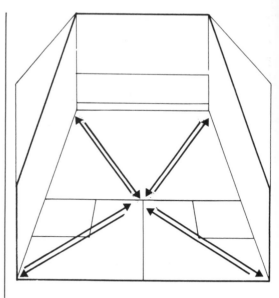

Starting from the T, try to touch as many corners as possible with either your hand or the racket in a set 30-40 second period.

Local muscle endurance

Standard tests for leg endurance, the most important for squash players, include squat thrusts, standing squats with arms extended, burpees (a combination of the two) or star jumps. Count your score for a set one-minute period.

Speed testing

Timed speed shuttle

Starting from the back wall, sprint to the rear line of the service box, followed by the short line, front wall, short line again, and finishing with the service box again. After every line, return to touch the back wall nick. Record your time for the shuttle and take the best of three. Follow the same sequence of movement for each test.

On and off court sprints

A straight flying sprint is the classic test of speed. On-court this means 3-5 full lengths; outside, a 40-yard dash is the best measure.

Strength testing

Broad jump

Similar to the long jump but without a run-up. From a standing position, bend the knees, swing the arms and leap forward as far as you can. Measure the distance from the start line for your score.

Grip dynamometer

Other than the legs, the grip is the only strength area that squash players need worry about. To test this, you need a simple dynamometer, which is available in most clubs or gyms. It gauges wrist strength by measuring energy exertion of the wrist in kilograms.

Standing vertical jump

To be fast off the mark, so crucial for any squash player, you need leg power. The standing jump tests leg power.

To test your leg power, stand next to a high-ceilinged wall with your arm stretched above your head. Make a mark on the wall as high as you can reach. Crouch down into a squatting position and leap up, making a new mark at the top of your jump. The difference between your two marks is the score. Take the best of three attempts.

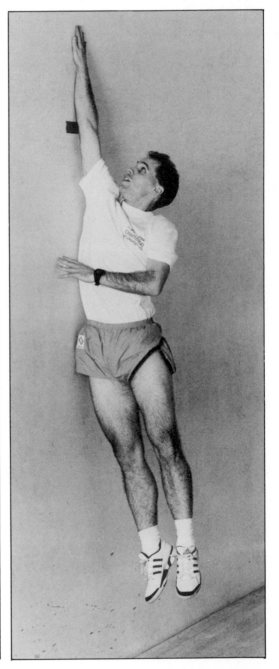

Flexibility testing

The hamstrings and quadriceps are the key areas requiring flexibility in a squash player and can be measured with a sit-and-reach test. Sit on the floor, with straight legs and toes pointing vertically; lean forwards and reach out to your toes. The distance between your fingers and toes, either positive or negative, is the score.

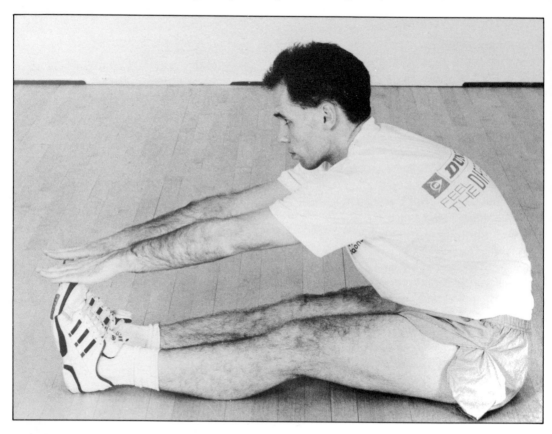

Testing procedure

Warm up thoroughly before doing any test. You can do all the tests individually, but they are often more effective if performed with a partner who can count scores or operate the stop-watch. Testing areas are flexible; even the on-court tests can be completed if you measure out a similar area outside. Finally, remember again that the main use of the tests is as a guide for an individual player and should not be compared to scores achieved by other players.

CHAPTER THREE

PREPARING TO TRAIN

Whatever your standard, a programme of fitness training will benefit your game. It could be to fine-tune and maintain an existing high level, or to improve one particular component such as speed, or provide a foundation for play. Fitness is only one component of your squash training – the importance you give to it depends on how limited you think your game is by a lack of fitness.

Although more on-court play will certainly improve your fitness, it is more efficient to attack the problem off-court, with a programme tailored to address your weaknesses. We will discuss the various components of the programme in the next chapter, but before you embark on a training plan, it is crucial to understand a few basic rules of training and the problems you are likely to encounter.

Understanding training

Plan and record
The cornerstone of any programme is the plan. Take account of your work and social commitments and organise your training around them. Ask yourself when and how often you can train. A well-planned schedule will help you train regularly and avoid the irritation of having to miss sessions due to conflicts. Start from day one and plan a month ahead. Write it down and make appointments with yourself. Keep the plan flexible, and alter it as other commitments change. Make a habit of using a training diary in which you can record each day's activities and test results, and make notes after each session on how you performed and how you felt. This will also help you track your progress over a specific time period.

Individual and relevant
There is a tendency with all players to concentrate on the aspects of fitness that they are good at. You have to be honest about your strengths and weaknesses because it is your weaknesses that let you down in a match. Just as with your on-court play, improvement comes when your weakness turns to strength, every programme is personal and has to be tailored to your own individual needs.

Remember also that your training programme must be geared to the individual physical demands of squash. You are not embarking on a general fitness programme – if you want to develop your squash fitness the training has to be relevant to squash. Developing the stamina of a marathon runner is not the type of aerobic preparation needed for a squash match, which, at most, will go to five games.

Finding motivation
If you are are not motivated, your training will suffer. Ask yourself why you want to be fitter and what you are aiming to achieve. Decide on your objectives and set yourself realistic attainable goals. Some people are more self-motivated than others, but there is no greater motivator than success. Evaluate your progress regularly using the tests outlined in Chapter 2; they will give you targets at which you aim. Add variety to your training by changing the venue,

duration and intensity of sessions. Boredom, inevitably, has a negative effect on motivation.

Progression

Your fitness is not going to change overnight. Improvement is gradual, and training loads have to be applied progressively. Work on a long-term plan that will allow your body to adapt gradually. If you try to build up too quickly the body will be unable to cope, increasing the risk of injury. If injury strikes, ensure that you are fully recovered before you start training again. Don't jump back into the programme where you left off, but build up again gradually to reach your former fitness level. Don't try to make up the lost time by working harder; just accept it and adjust your training targets accordingly.

Overload

Within each session, aim to build up gradually to a point of overload. Improvements in strength, flexibility or endurance result from additional stress on the body. This can be achieved by increasing the resistance, duration or intensity of work, or by decreasing rest time.

Balance and consistency

One of the basic tenets of a training programme is balance. Hard sessions, such as intensive speed work-outs or demanding anaerobic practices, should be balanced with easier aerobic or flexibility sessions. This is particularly relevant if you are putting in more than one session a day. Avoid successive hard practices, or your body will have difficulty coping. If you want to do speed work and anaerobic work in the same session, do the speed work first.

Linked to balance is consistency. It is easier to maintain than to attain. Aerobic endurance can disappear in a third of the time it takes to build it up. Try to maintain a consistent and regular regime, avoiding long periods of inactivity which will be detrimental to progress.

Rest and recovery

Never consider a rest day a wasted day. Quality training time is far more important than mere quantity. To get the best from your training, it is essential to give your body sufficient time to recover from a demanding work-out. Any fitness programme must include at least one day a week of rest. Don't forget your sleep; it is equally important to ensure that you get a good night's sleep every day.

Distractions

Inevitably there will always be distractions to training. Good planning and organization will help keep them to a minimum, but they are something you must overcome to attain your training goals.

Warming to fitness

Warming-up is one of the most underestimated and under-utilized elements of any training programme. For too many players, warming-up means no more than a few casual stretches before leaping into the day's training, practice session or match. Is it any wonder that these players are mysteriously plagued by injury or seem to have the reputation of being slow starters? Of course, time to train and play is always limited, but you are doing yourself no favours by passing up the warm-up in the interests of saving time. Think of your body as the machine it is. It can no more jump from a cold start to peak performance without damage than any other engine or machine.

If you warm up a car engine it performs more efficiently – the same applies to the muscles and tendons of the body. A thorough warm-up will make them more elastic and hence less likely to pull or tear when subjected to sudden stresses. Any stiffness or tension will also be eased from the muscles and joints. The warm-up will raise the body temperature and heart rate, and by the time you are ready to start the day's training you should already be perspiring lightly. It has an additional advantage in that not only does it fully prepare your body for strenuous exercise but it also allows you to focus your mind and concentrate without distraction.

A complete warm-up routine should have three stages: warmers, stretches and mobilizers. Allow 10-15 minutes, or slightly longer in cold conditions, to complete the routine.

Warmers

These are a series of gentle exercises intended to warm the muscles before stretching. A sample routine might start with 15 seconds easy running on the spot, followed by another 15 seconds running with the knees up to the chest. Now bring the arms into it by pointing your fists up into the air and punching up alternately with each arm for a further 15-20 seconds. Finish off by standing with feet astride and hands high in the air. Rotate the torso in a circular motion bringing the hands down to the ground and back up above your head in a clockwise direction. Change after 10 rotations to rotate in an anti-clockwise direction. Experiment with other simple warm-ups and develop your own routine.

Stretches

Now your muscles are warm they will stretch more easily. You are aiming at the muscle groups that are specific to squash and squash training. All the stretches should be performed statically – don't bounce up and down, but try to maintain a relaxed sustained stretch position with a passive pull. Hold each stretch for a count of 10 and repeat it three times. As with all your training, try to develop good habits. Don't rush it; start with a preliminary stretch before progressing into the main one, don't stretch to the point of pain and avoid bouncing. The following warm-up stretch routine covers all the major muscle groups involved in squash. Again, develop a programme that you are happy with, and tailor it to the particular training you intend to do each day.

Wrist stretch

1 Grip your open right hand around the wrist with your left hand, keeping the thumb below the knuckle of the little finger at the back of the right hand.

2 Apply pressure with the thumb pushing the right hand round and stretching the wrist.

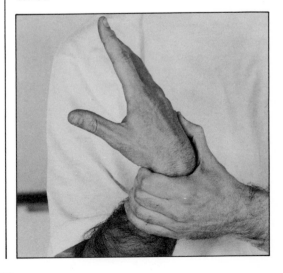

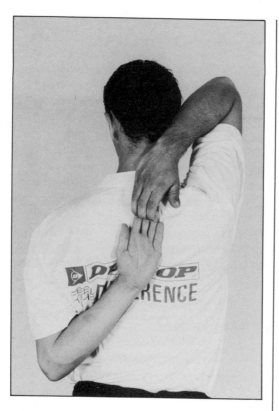

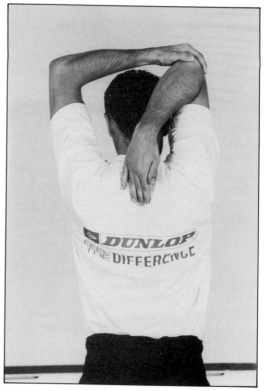

Shoulder stretch *above*

Reach down your back with one hand and up with the other, trying to bring the two together, then pull hard in opposite directions. If your hands don't meet, get a training partner to slowly ease them together.

Bent arm shoulder stretch *above*

Bend your right arm above your head, hold the elbow with your left hand and gently pull it towards your left shoulder.

Upper back stretch *opposite*

Hold your hands together behind your back and lift.

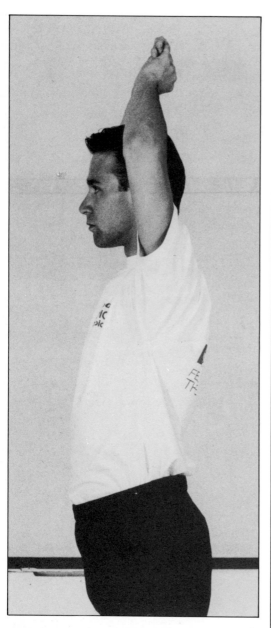

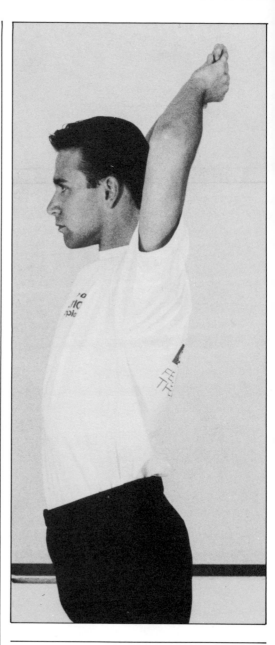

Above-head shoulder stretch *above*

Hold your arms together above your head and pull down.

Lower back stretch *opposite*

Lie on the ground, arch your back and bring your legs over your head.

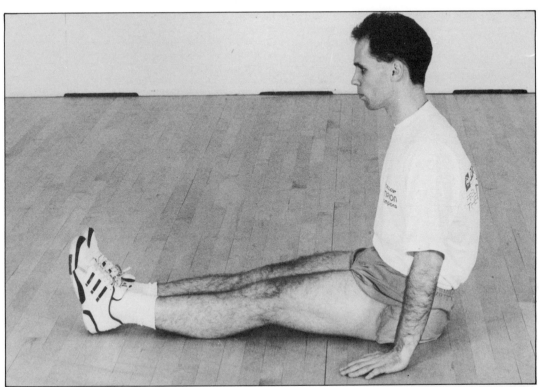

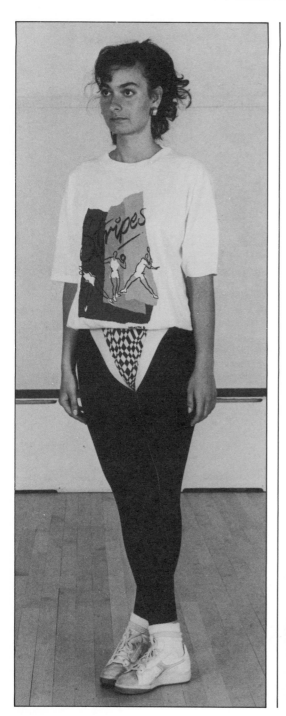

Crossed leg standing hamstring stretch

1 Stand with one leg crossed over the other.

2 Bend over and touch your toes with your fingers. Alternate by switching from leg to leg. The same exercise can be done with feet together rather than crossed.

Sitting quadriceps stretch

1 Sit on the floor with your legs tucked underneath you.

2 Lean backwards and push your hips forward while gently supporting your body with your hands. This may be uncomfortable on a hard floor.

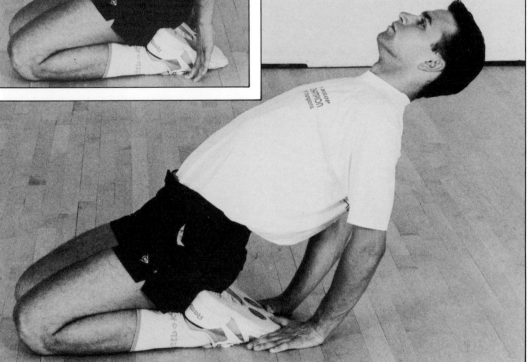

 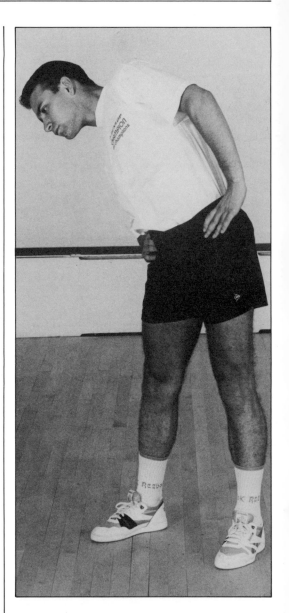

Hip torso stretch

Standing with legs apart, slowly rotate your body from the waist, stretching as far as possible to each side, first in a clockwise direction, then anti-clockwise.

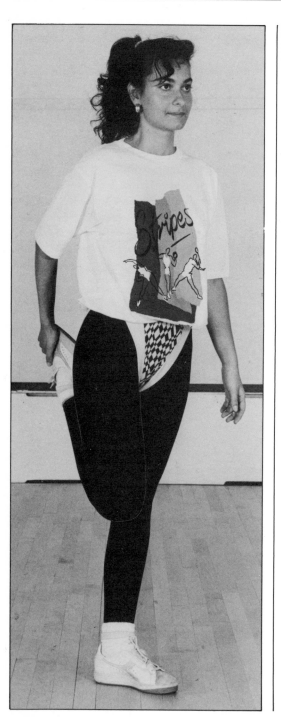

One-leg quadriceps stretch
left

1 Stand on one leg and pull the other leg up to your buttock.
2 Keep a tight grip on the leg and try to straighten it. You may have to balance yourself against a wall.

Two-leg sitting stretch
above right

Sitting with straight legs, bend forwards and try to put your head on your knees. This also stretches the hamstrings and quads.

Trunk stretch *below right*

1 Sit with one leg straight and the other bent and crossed over it, placing the foot at the outside of the knee.
2 Turn your body to the bent knee, resting the opposite elbow on the outside of it, and twist.

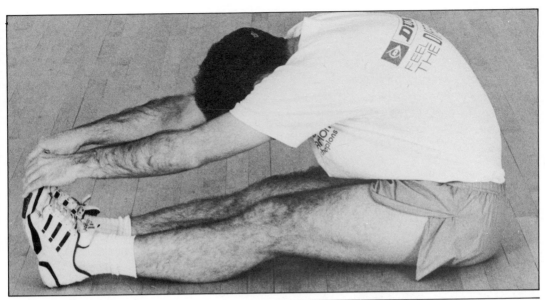

Straight leg sitting stretch

above

1 Sit with legs straight and as far apart as possible.

2 Bend forward from the waist, with your head up and back straight.

Adductor stretch *right*

1 Stand with feet wide apart. Bend one leg and keep the other straight.

2 Put the weight on the straight leg and stretch towards the opposite leg.

Bent leg sitting stretch
above
1 Sit with knees bent and the soles of your feet together.
2 Keep the knees close to the floor, grip the feet and lean forwards from the hips.

Raised hamstring stretch *right*
1 Put one heel on a raised surface in front of you at hip level.
2 Lean forwards and try to put your head on your knees.

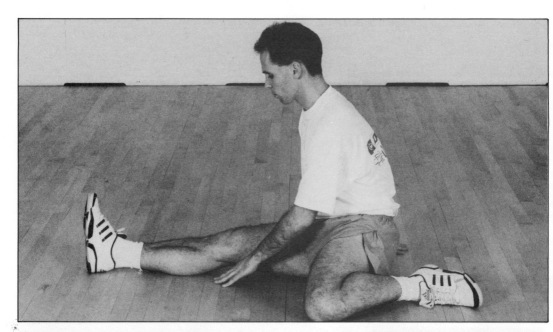

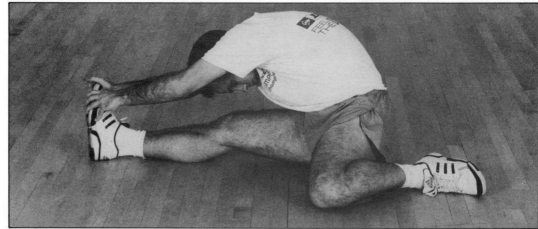

Hurdler's hamstring stretch
above

1 Sit with one leg straight in front of you and the other tucked up behind and to the side.

2 Stretch forwards from the waist over the front leg, keeping the back straight and head up. Hold for 10 and switch legs.

Standing calf stretch *right*

1 Stand up straight. Lean forwards against a wall and push back your feet as far as possible but keep your heels on the ground. This can be done with feet together or with one in front of the other.

Squatting calf stretch

Stand with feet flat on the ground, bend the knees and bring your legs down as far over the ankles as possible. Keep your heels on the ground.

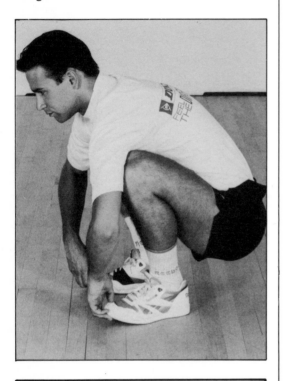

Design your own warm-up stretch programme for the variety of exercises illustrated, but make sure that you choose at least one stretch from each of the various muscle groups.

Mobilizers

Now that you are fully stretched, it is safe to move on to mobilizing exercises. These are rapid free-moving exercises intended to further loosen the joints after the stretch. Again there are numerous exercises from which to choose. Some of the most popular include: arm circling and swinging, side bends, knee bends and hip circling.

Start off with some arm circling to further loosen the shoulders and playing arm. Take large free swings moving both arms together in a clockwise direction for 20 seconds, then reverse. Hip circling is similar to the hip torso stretch illustrated on page 28. Use rapid circular movements to shift your weight from one leg then the other. Follow this with a short series of side bends, stand with feet apart and move from side to side stretching your outside arm out over your head as you bend. On the knee bends, go down slowly but push up strongly, keeping your back straight as you come up. After 2-3 minutes of fast mobilizers, you are ready to start your training programme proper.

Ensure that you arrive at your training session in good time so that you do not have to rush through the warm-up. Experiment with various combinations of exercises to find the ones you are comfortable with. When you finally decide on one, stick with it. You are aiming for a situation where the warm-up becomes a training ritual – a routine that you subconsciously follow no matter how you feel on the day.

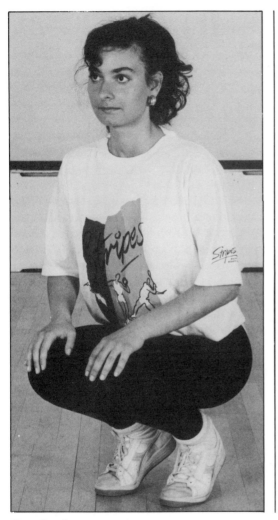

Knee bends

Side bends

The cool-down

A final post-training word. When you have finished your session, don't immediately jump into the shower or bar. Take five minutes to cool down slowly. After any vigorous exercise there is a build-up of waste products in the muscles. If you warm down with some gentle jogging or stretching, the blood supply to the muscle tissue continues long enough to flush out this lactic acid and enzyme waste. This will help prevent muscle soreness and stiffness the following day, especially if it was a particularly hard session.

CHAPTER FOUR

TRAINING

Endurance

Running, and steady pace runs form the ideal foundation around which to build an aerobic endurance programme. With all aerobic endurance training, you should be working at a sustainable level of between 80-90 per cent of your maximum. The idea is to maintain a continuous pace for a prolonged period of time, causing you to breathe heavily but not to a point of exhaustion.

However, if you are not used to running, it will take time to build stamina for target runs of 25-30 minutes. Start with much shorter runs of around 5-10 minutes and progress gradually over a four-week period adding 5 minutes a week. There is no need to extend your runs beyond 30 minutes – this is sufficient to build up the aerobic endurance required by most club players.

Ideally these long continuous runs should be at about 90 per cent of maximum effort. To find this maximum, measure out a 3-4 mile course and run it as fast as possible. Add 10 per cent to this time to obtain your training time. It is a good idea to record where the mile markers are when you originally measure out the course – it will help you track your pace during the run. Remember that you are aiming to maintain a consistent speed throughout; for most club players, it falls between 7-8 minute mile pace. Retest yourself regularly over the same course and adjust your training pace as your times improve. You should be running at least three times a week when initially trying to build up aerobic endurance.

Fartlek (varied pace running)

This develops a combination of aerobic and anaerobic endurance. It works on a base of continuous pace running interspersed with faster legs. Almost any combination is possible, working on either time or distance. You can have equal periods of fast and slow running or you can weight it in favour of one or the other. The slower pace should be around 70-75 per cent of maximum, with the faster periods between 95-100 per cent. A common mistake in fartlek is to run too slowly in the steady pace period and turn the session into an interval practice. A sample fartlek session might include:

5 minutes training pace.
4 x 1 minute at 95 per cent followed by 1 minute slow pace.
6 x 20-second sprints followed by 1 minute recovery jog.
3 minutes medium pace.
4 x 30-second sprints with 45 seconds recovery jog.
5 minutes at training pace and cool-down.

There is no set combination, and you should design your own, but put the faster sections at the end. Use the principle of progression to extend the sprint and shorten the recovery jogs.

Hill running

This is excellent for building muscle endurance in the legs. Look for a hill that will take 2-3 minutes to climb; the gradient should allow you to continue running throughout. Grass is often the best hill surface, especially in the descent where there is a lot of pressure on the knee and ankle joints. Run up the hill and jog down it to recover. A typical hill session would involve 10 continuous climbs with no rest period.

A note of warning: always run in running shoes. Squash shoes have a relatively thin sole and do not have the cushioning or stability to protect the knee and ankle joints during a long run. Grass is easier on the feet than tarmac or concrete, but you should try to vary the surface. Running too much on the roads can cause injuries so it is always better to train on grass. Beginners should not run on consecutive days.

Other aerobic endurance training

If you find running a little tedious or you are injured, you may find some solace in alternative aerobic training.

Cycling

This is an excellent form of training for the all-important quadricep muscles and for general cardio-respiratory endurance. As with all exercises, build up slowly from a short 15 minute cycle to a maximum of about 45 minutes. On a stationary bike, start with 5 minutes and slowly increase to 20 minutes, at a moderate resistance. Check your pulse at the end of a session – you should be working at 80 per cent of maximum (calculate your maximum by deducting your age from a rate of 220 beats per minute).

Swimming

This is a good substitute for running to improve aerobic endurance if injury strikes or as gentle exercise to follow an intensive strength or anaerobic session. Most pools have special roped-off lanes for swimming laps. Start with 10 minutes continuous swimming (touch and go at the end of each length and do not rest), and gradually increase to 30 minutes, maintaining the same pace even when stepping up time in the water. Target effort is around 70 per cent of maximum pulse rate. Either breast stroke or crawl will provide a testing workout, although crawl is better for players with any knee problems.

Skipping

This is often used by boxers to improve stamina, footwork and timing, but it has the same benefits for squash players. Start with 100 skips hopping from foot to foot. It will take time to master the technique but your final target is 130 skips a minute for 25 minutes. Vary the steps to practise co-ordination and timing.

Interval training

This is the mainstay of your anaerobic endurance training. By necessity, it involves stop-start bursts of activity at an intensity above the level at which the lungs and respiratory system can supply the muscles with oxygen. The cool-down is especially important after such a session to help remove waste products from the system and overcome stiffness.

All interval training is split between short

periods of work and recovery. It usually means sprints on a track but could equally be cycling, skipping, speed shuttles or conditioning exercises at maximum intensity. A standard session starts with six intensive 30-second bursts of activity followed by a 30 second rest. Build up each session to 12 intervals. When you can do this, add 5 seconds per interval, so that you are working for 35 seconds. Increase in 5-second increments over a number of sessions to a maximum of 12 sets of 45 seconds followed by 45-second rest periods. Most people are unable to sustain an anaerobic work rate for interval sets of longer than 45 seconds.

It helps to work with a partner who can keep track of times while you are exercising. Alternate the rest and exercise periods between the two of you. If you are doing shuttle runs or court sprints, count the number of lines or walls you touch, making sure that you reach the same number in each successive set. Sprint intervals on a running track can be by distance, starting with, say, 200m, rather than by time. Increase the distance by 20m, gradually building up to 300m intervals. Remember that intensive anaerobic training should be the last sessions of any day.

Circuit training

This builds up a combination of aerobic and anaerobic endurance. A balanced circuit will not only improve local muscle endurance but it will also create greater cardio-respiratory endurance. The aim is to exercise at a level below maximum intensity for a prolonged period of time.

When designing a circuit, start with at least 8 body weight exercises, each concentrating on a different area of the body. Plan the rotation of exercises to avoid working the same muscle groups consecutively. The most common circuits require you to complete a set number of repetitions against the clock. Calculate the ideal number of repetitions by testing yourself in each exercise for a set one-minute period, and resting for one minute between exercises. Take the test score and halve it for your training rate – for example, if you can do 40 press-ups in a minute you should be doing 20 press-ups in each circuit.

Start with two complete circuits, performing each exercise as quickly as possible. Do not rest in between. Ensure that you have mastered the correct technique for each exercise and don't sacrifice it in the interests of speed. Build up gradually to a maximum of 10 circuits. As the circuit becomes easier, add some extra exercises, retest yourself every two weeks and adjust your training rate to any improvement. The circuit training session should last a maximum of 30 minutes, three times a week.

Alternate circuits test performance in set time periods. For example, in a five-minute circuit you do 10 selected exercises each for 30 seconds, trying to maximize repetitions. Another option is pyramid circuits, where you start, say, with eight repetitions and build up to 14 in increments of two, before working down to eight again.

The use of a training diary is particularly important in circuit training. Record your exercises, your training rates, your times for each circuit and any changes or improvements you make. Without a diary you will have no idea of progress.

Circuit training exercises

Press-ups
1 Lie face down on the ground.
2 Push the body up until your arms are straight and lower again. Keep the body horizontal and the back straight. Women find it easier to rest on their knees.

Sit-ups

1 Lie on your back with knees slightly bent and raised.

2 Cross your arms in front and raise your body until your arms touch your thighs. Keep the back straight and bend from the abdomen.

Sit-ups with twist

Follow the same action as for an ordinary sit-up, but put your hands on the side of your head to avoid damaging the neck muscles. Keep your neck straight and twist the torso as you rise to touch the right knee with the left elbow. Alternate elbows.

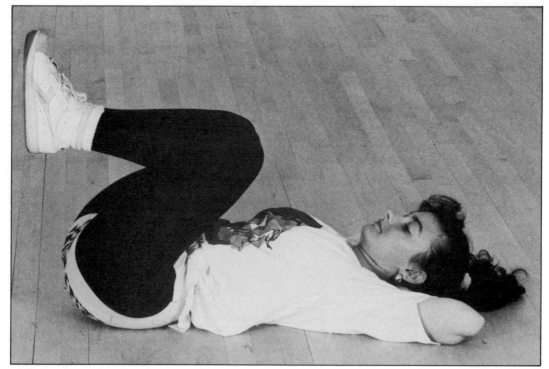

Leg raises

1 Lie on your back with legs straight and hands behind your head.

2 Raise your legs six inches and then lower to just above the ground. Repeat. Do alternate leg raises, bringing the knees up to the chest and straighten.

Squat thrusts

1 Crouch down with knees bent between your arms.

2 Keeping the hands still, force the legs back until straight. Return the legs to the original position. This exercise can be varied to alternate legs backwards and forwards from a sprint start.

Burpees

This is the same thrust but also includes a standing squat at the end of the action.

Bench steps

Step on and off the bench one foot at a time. Stand straight when both feet are on the bench.

Astride jumps

1 Stand with your feet astride a bench.
2 Jump continuously on and off the bench.

Bench jumps *right*

1 Stand with feet together on one side of a bench.
2 Keep the feet together and jump over the bench continuously from side to side.

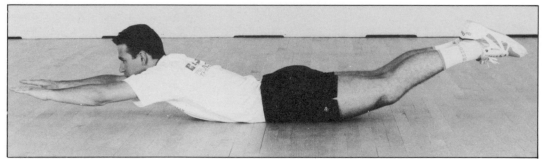

Back arches *above*
1 Lie face down with your arms extended above your head.
2 Lift the arms, shoulders and legs off the ground together. Hold the position, then lower and repeat.

Star jumps *left*
Start standing, then squat down and jump up. Force your arms and legs out to form a star shape. Return to the squat position and repeat.

Swing-overs

1 Stand with feet astride and arms extended over the head.

2 Rotate the body at the hips, swing low and touch the ground on either side of the feet.

Diagonal toe touches

1 Stand with feet wide apart.
2 Bend over and touch the left foot with the right hand, followed swiftly by the right foot with the left hand.

Squat and twist

1 Squat down with the arms extended in front.
2 Stand up and twist the arms to the side.
3 Squat down and repeat to the other side. Rest your heels on a piece of wood for support.

 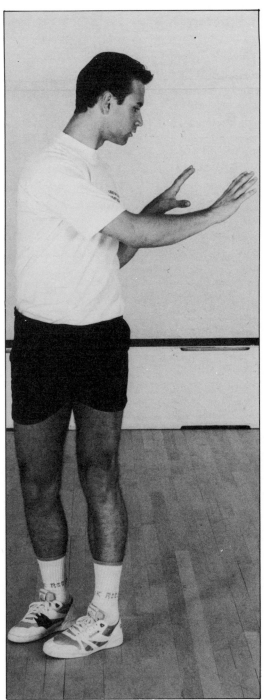

Flexibility

To play squash does not require a great amount of flexibility, but it does help. The more flexible and supple you are, the easier you will find it to move around the court and the more responsive your body will be when asked to perform a sudden lunge or over-stretch to make a tough pick-up. You also reduce the chance of muscle or tendon injury, particularly when the movement is unexpected, such as slipping on a patch of sweat.

Although most of the exercises are the same as those used in warm-up stretching, the nature of flexibility training and its purpose are quite different. A warm-up is essential exercise preparation: to raise the body temperature and pulse, and extend muscles and tendons to their maximum elasticity. A long-term flexibility programme aims to push beyond the maximum, thereby increasing overall flexibility. In technical terms, warm-up stretching pushes against the muscles' protective reflex or stretch reflex. Longer flexibility exercises work on the tendon in what is known as the inverse stretch reflex.

The main areas on which to concentrate are the hamstring, quad and adductor muscles, but a degree of wrist and shoulder flexibility is also important in squash. Create a flexibility programme from the stretches described on page 21 and rather than choosing just one exercise for each muscle set, choose a variety. Follow the same principles of stretching, again avoiding bouncing, which stiffens rather than loosening muscles. Start by holding each stretch for 10-15 seconds and gradually build up to 60 seconds. The total session should last approximately 45 minutes, but a longer session will not have any negative effects. Don't be disheartened if you don't see immediate improvement; it takes time to develop greater muscle and joint flexibility. A passive stretching session is the ideal exercise to follow on intensive speed, strength or endurance practice, which often has a negative effect on flexibility.

Strength

A quick glance at any of the top squash players in the world should tell you that strength alone is not the key to the game. Nevertheless, a certain amount of body strength in specific areas is necessary. Leg strength is important to brake, support the body and drive off to reach difficult balls. A solid grip also requires good wrist and forearm strength, to stop the racket twisting in your hand and help you dig out shots from poor positions. Before embarking on a muscle strengthening programme examine your problem carefully. What you perceive to be a lack of strength is more often a deficiency of your technique or timing.

The essence of training with weights to develop strength is the opposite of weight training to build endurance. Rather than low-weight high repetitions, you need relatively high weights and a low number of repetitions. Ideal training weights are approximately 80 per cent of your maximum lift. Start with a much lower weight to master the technique. Exercises are designed to isolate particular muscle groups, and if you do not follow the correct technique you are liable to work the wrong groups or injure yourself. When you feel confident of the technique, move on to your training weight and do 8-10 quick repetitions in three sets. Rest time between sets should be kept to a minimum to maintain intensity levels. A successful strength programme requires constant increases in weight, and you should retest your maximum lift every fortnight and reassess your training weight accordingly.

Do not exercise the same muscle groups twice in any 48-hour period. Make the strength session the last training of the day and do not play squash afterwards. The best time to do heavy strength work-outs is in the off season, ideally finishing a month before the season starts.

The best way to balance your training programme to build up for the season is discussed in Chapter 4.

Strength training exercises

All the exercises can be performed either with free weights or at a multi-station gym. Consult an instructor before starting your programme. If you are working with free weights, train with a partner who can spot for you. Design your own weight-training programme from the exercises described.

Wrist rolls
Holding the bar with the weight suspended between your hands, wind the weight up to the bar, then unwind it again.

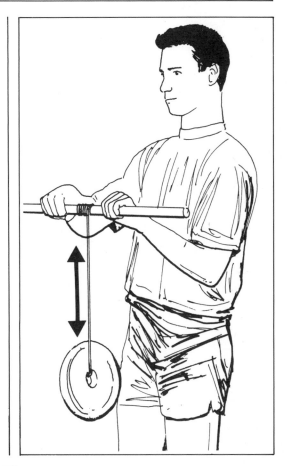

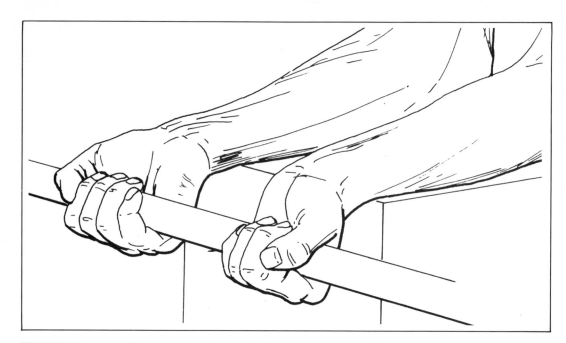

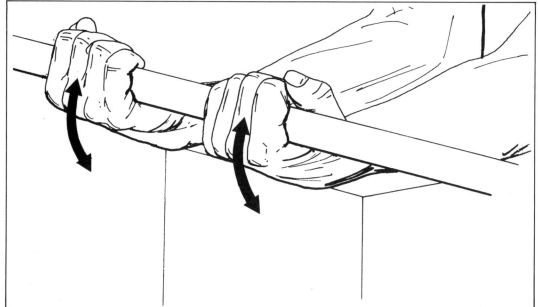

Forearm curls

1 Place both arms flat on a bench.

2 Lift the bar towards you from the wrists without lifting your arms.

Bicep curls

1 Stand with your legs slightly apart and elbows resting by your side.

2 Bend your arms from the elbows and bring the weight up to below your chin, then lower. Keep the elbows tightly by your side and your back straight.

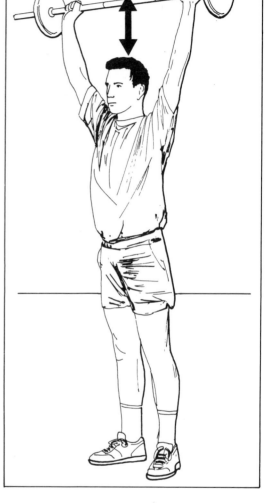

Military press

1 Stand with the weight resting behind your neck.

2 Lift the weight into the air and extend your arms fully above your head.

3 Hold and lower the weight behind your head. Alternatively, start with the bar resting on the top of your chest and press above the head, hold and return.

Bench press

1 Lie flat on a bench, holding the bar above your chest with arms fully extended.

2 Lower it to the chest and press up again. This exercise can be performed with a weighted bar or two dumbells.

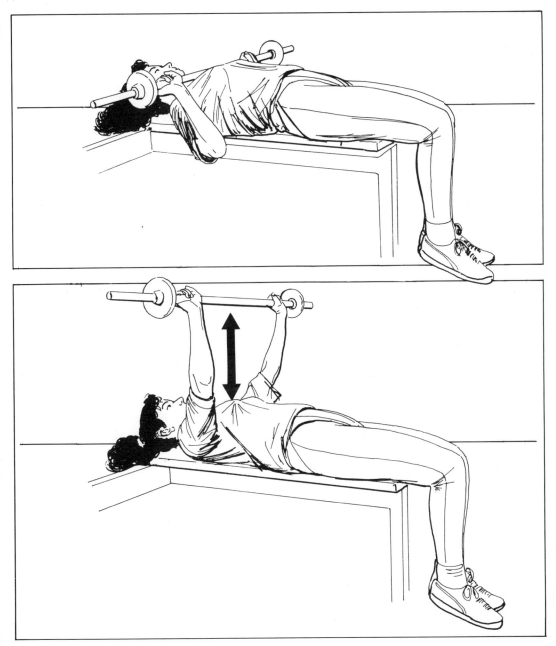

Incline sit-ups *above*

1 Lie on a sit-up bench with your arms crossed in front of you.

2 Raise your body so that your arms touch your knees. Make the exercise more difficult by making the bench steeper or holding a weight behind your head.

Half squats *right*

1 Stand with legs apart and the bar resting behind your shoulders.

2 Squat down with a straight back, and lower your body until the thighs are at right angles to your calves. Put something under your heels for support.

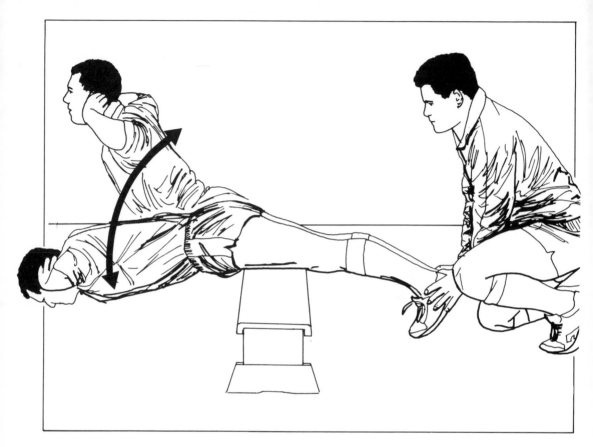

Back arches *above*

1 Secure your feet and support yourself below the waist.
2 With your hands behind your head, bend forwards at the waist.
3 Lift yourself up again until your back is straight. Don't over-extend your back.

Leg press (on a multi-gym)
above right

1 Sit with legs bent on the press platform.
2 Push the legs forwards until straight and then return to the original position.

Leg curls (on a multi-gym)
below right

1 Lie face down with your heels behind the curl bar.
2 Grip firmly with the hands and pull the bar forwards until it touches your bottom.

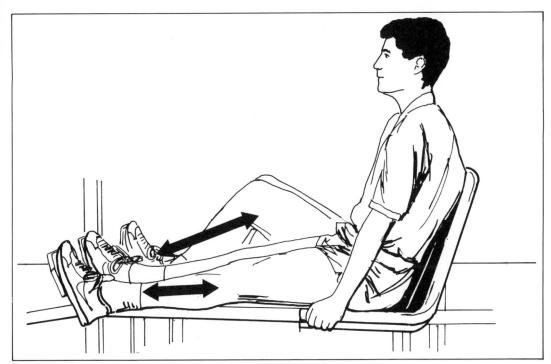

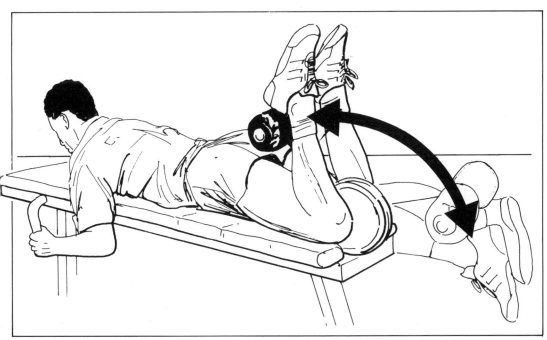

Lunges

1 Stand with your feet one in front of the other and the bar resting on the front of the chest, with elbows forward.

2 Lunge forwards, bending the legs and pushing the hips forwards and down.

Calf raises

1 Step, with toes only, on to the edge of a low bench supporting the bar on your shoulders.

2 Come up on your toes and then back down again.

Speed

Speed can be improved and trained by improving muscle speed. Initially this is best achieved with a basic strength programme and then by using specific speed drills.

It is important, however, to realize that your speed on a squash court is not simply a matter of fast sprinting speed or of quick muscle movement but, as with football, the first steps are in the mind – when, where and how you move are the important things. You may be a very fast sprinter when under way, but if it takes you a long time to get out of the blocks you are not going to be very successful.

Reading the game and the transferring of weight on to the appropriate take-off foot make the difference. Anticipation is in the mind, and the reaction time from the moment the ball is sighted until movement begins involves reflexes as well as muscles.

Anticipation can be learnt by studying your opponents. Before they hit, ask yourself which shot is coming next. Study the player position in relation to the ball, body position and backswing, and use your experience of players to work out the likely shot.

Practise your reflexes on court in solo practice with hard fast volleys close to the front (straight and alternating) and with hard reflex drives in front at the short line. Practise by having a partner or coach fire hard balls for you to intercept.

Efficient, smooth, rhythmic movement is more important in a game than outright speed, and this must be borne in mind when training for speed and must be worked on on court. Concentrate on coming back to a ready position after each shot with your weight forward on the balls of your feet. Practise recovering by pushing back to the T as you pull out of your swing.

Leg strength programme

Before embarking on speed training it is advisable to use a basic leg strengthening programme for two to four weeks. Use multigym equipment concentrating on stations that exercise the quads, hamstrings and calf muscles. To develop strength, use heavy loads and a small number of reps – say, 10. Select a load at which you can just complete a set of 10 repetitions with about 10 seconds between each, performing each exercise as fast as possible. Repeat 5 or 10 minutes later and possibly for a third time. Alternate upper and lower body work. Carry out the programme three times a week.

Speed programme

Your speed programme can be made up of a mixture of four components: speed shuttles, sprints, skipping and plyometrics. Speed shuttles and skipping, or speed shuttles and plyometrics, or plyometrics and sprinting can be performed together but not just skipping and plyometrics.

Warming up thoroughly is crucial before speed work. Wear proper cushioned shoes and work on a good floor surface.

Speed shuttles

On court (or in a gym or other suitable space) use bursts of movement for 10 seconds at maximum speed followed by 50 seconds rest. Do 6, 8 or 10 reps and progress to two sets with 10 minutes between each. Various movements can be used – sprinting lengths, corner running from the T and ghosting (shadow play).

Sprints

Set two marks 20 metres apart, and sprint from the first as fast as possible, decelerating after the second to a gentle walk.

Repeat after 30 seconds, do 6 reps and stop or, if appropriate, complete another set after a 10-minute rest.

Skipping

Skip at an alternate-leg speed of 180 skips per minute for 30 seconds, with 2 minutes rest. Perform 6 to 10 reps. Skip on a soft surface such as a carpet or sprung floor wearing cushioned shoes.

Plyometrics (rebound jumping)

Be careful not to overdo plyometrics initially. Gradually increase the sets and the weekly frequency.

1 Depth jumping

Use two stable stools, boxes or chairs about 40cm/16 inches high, and placed a suitable distance apart on a suitable material such as a carpet. Jump down from one and immediately rebound as high as possible. Then jump/step on to the other chair, turn and repeat the movement after regaining your balance. A set of 10 jumps should be followed by a few minutes rest. Perform a number of sets but stop once quality begins to deteriorate.

2 Bench bounding

Use an ordinary gymnasium-type bench about 25-30cm/10-12 inches high. Stand with feet together at one end, jumping down with feet astride, and then up together again. Progress along the bench like this. The number of sets is again determined by when quality deteriorates.

On court

Shuttle running

Perhaps the most convenient option you have for interval training is on-court shuttle running. Often this can be fitted in after a practice session or game. As well as sprinting lengths, various exercises can be used to practise squash movements and help balance, agility and speed on court. Your ability to move around the court well depends on how well you stop, change direction, turn, lunge and recover.

Work for 30 seconds at maximum intensity on one or more of the exercises below, then rest for 30 seconds. Start with about six sets and build towards twelve. Gradually increase the intervals by 5 seconds until you reach 45 seconds. Once the number of repetitions within an interval time are established, this is a convenient way to work, although these should be reassessed periodically.

1 Lengths Run lengths of the court, bending and touching about tin high at each end.

2 Half lengths Run from the short line to the front. Run backwards to the short line and change direction to run forwards again to the front.

3 Backwards running and turning From the back wall run to the front and touch. Run backwards to the short line, change direction and run forwards to the back again. Repeat.

4 Lunging Step across your body and lunge to the side, bending to touch in front of your toe. Push back and repeat on the other side.

5 Sidesteps and lunge From a ready position, sidestep across court and lunge on the front foot, reaching to touch the side. Push back and sidestep across court and lunge on the other side.

6 Four touches From the back, run to the back of the service box, touch the line and return to the back. Repeat to the short line and return to the back. Repeat at the three-quarter mark and to the front.

Speed shuttles are discussed on page 66 can also involve the four touches exercise described above.

Ghosting

This is interval training using simulated squash movements of rallies and strokes. While building stamina you are practising squash movement and stroking as well as using the same muscles that you would utilize in a game. Jonah Barrington, innovator of this method of squash training, says, 'The object of "ghosting" is to simulate the playing of a game as closely as possible, but in so doing one is in fact putting the body under much greater stress, more frequently, than would happen in a game.'

Initially, before attempting it, it is best to use repetitive movements rather slowly to practise and groove the strokes before attempting them at maximum. For a ghosting session, use the same times as for shuttle running and attempt to simulate the squash movement and stroke as accurately as possible. Start each burst from a ready position, crouched with weight forward over the toes and racket up. Attempt to return to this position in the ghosted rally. Many ghosted rallies can be developed but on page 70 are some basic patterns.

Ghosted exercises

1 Front corners From the T, run to the right front corner and play a straight drive. Return to the T and repeat on the left. Alternatively, play a drop or a drop disguised with full swing.

2 Back corners From a ready position, turn and run jump to the back, preparing by turning the body and taking the racket back as you go. Crouch in a strong stance, play a straight drive, return to the T and repeat on the other side. Alternatively, boast.

3 Right side From the T, move for a forehand drive, forehand volley and back-corner drive, returning to the T after each shot.

4 Left side Repeat on the left.

5 Whole court Play the six shots used above. Various movement patterns may be used.

Random ghosting

Play an imaginary rally of random squash shots simulating squash movement, especially movement to and from the T.

Partner ghosting

One player ghosts, while the other stands in the front and either calls the stations a player must run to (i.e. 'one' or 'three') or points at them. Changing stations and shots before a player has a chance to return to the T can provide useful change of direction practice and some fun.

Solo practice

A good exercise that can be used in place of shuttles and in which you practise lunging, playing shots, recovering and repeating this pattern very quickly is the front corner boasting exercise.

Use a hot (and maybe a faster) ball. First, learn the exercise by playing the boast to rebound off the opposite wall and later to bounce on the floor before rebounding so that it can be boasted again. Practise sequences of, say, 20 or 30 shots and repeat as you would shuttles.

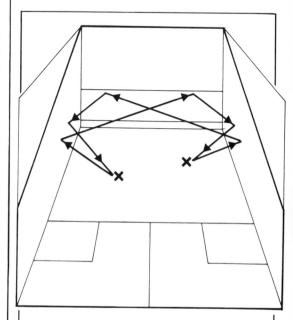

Solo practice: boasting side to side.

Pairs practice

Pairs practice on court with the ball can be useful in building endurance – both aerobic and anaerobic. Intervals of several minutes of high intensity exercise, followed by appropriate rests build aerobic endurance. Intervals of under 1 minute's exercise at maximum intensity build anaerobic endurance. Get into a rhythm on the exercises and try not to make mistakes.

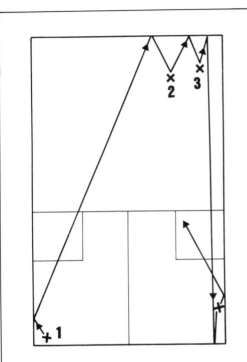

Pairs practise: use the (1) boast, (2) drop, (3) drive exercise for movement and stamina.

1 Boast, drop, drive Player A boasts, B drops straight, A drives straight, B boasts, etc. Here both players are working very hard over the diagonal. Keep this up for several minutes, rest, then change sides.

2 Fast boast Player A in the front court drives hard and a foot or so out from the wall for B to volley boast each side. Keep up this fast movement for 1 minute, rest, change and repeat several times.

Pressure

A coach (or one player feeding another) can apply pressure in any on-court exercise to raise the intensity sufficiently for interval

training. This has the advantage of building stamina, while the player learns to handle pressure situations, technically, tactically and mentally.

Pressure exercises

1 Three-corner exercises The coach, anchored in the back right corner, feeds the ball to the front left (with boasts and volley boasts), front right (with drops and volley drops) and back right (with straight drives and straight volleys) for the player to play to the back right corner, using crosscourts and lobs, straight drives and straight lobs, and straight drives respectively. Volley feeds add pressure.

A three-corner exercise can be fed from the front corners as well as the back.

2 Diagonal boasting The coach (or player B) feeds a cross-court drive for player A to boast, then a short drop for a front corner boast, followed by another crosscourt and drop and so on. Player A is worked back and forth on the diagonal.

3 Straight drive: random feeding The coach, C (or player B), feeds random shots about the court for A to straight drive. C continues feeding, moving from side to side.

4 Boasts: random feeding The coach (or player B) feeds random shots about the court for A to boast. C moves from side to side in the front.

Pressure session

A squash practice session on court can be made up of a combination of squash practices, pressure exercises, shuttles and ghosting. For example, the periods after ghosting or shuttles can be followed by periods of squash practice.

CHAPTER FIVE

YOUR PROGRAMME

We introduced this book with the premise that fitness was an important part of playing squash and crucial in progressing your game but added the proviso that this did not exclude developing other areas of your game – technique, shots, tactics and temperament – with solo practice, pairs practice, practice games and matches.

The challenge of pursuing fitness activities and of fitting these into a fitness programme, needs to be balanced with your squash activities. Fitness is just part of your overall programme, and attempts to improve your game should not be restricted to fitness alone. Successful attempts at improving your game should concentrate on your individual needs in both areas, and the activities selected must fit in with your lifestyle.

Very simply, there are two main seasons in your training: off season and in season. During the off season, fitness is the main activity, along with skill development. This is the time when fitness is built up. In season, the focus moves to playing, practising and maintaining fitness levels plus improving speed and movement.

Although Jahangir Khan has the reptuation of being one of the fittest players in the game, he does the majority of his off-court work in the close season.

Planning a fitness programme

Successful training must be planned. Use the following steps to think through what you want to do.

Assess	Consider where you are at. What is your potential, what are your weaknesses, limitations and problems?
Goals	Set realistic goals. Use the fitness tests.
Steps	Set out clear and specific steps that will take you to your goals.
Timetable	Plan blocks of time for each main step.
Select activities	Use the training section to select activities.
Record activities	Keep a record of your training and results.
Evaluate	Use the experience of a programme to help develop your next one.

Progress and balance

Build up your training gradually. Start with something at which you can be successful and then progress it. Think long-term and don't expect immediate results. For example, if you lack stamina, start running daily; in one week you will be tired, in six weeks you will be fitter with more endurance.

Balance your fitness training. Alternate hard and easy days, always allowing an easy day after hard anaerobic training. Work at speed training when you are fresh, and make anaerobic sessions the last of the day.

Rest is an important part of your programme. Take at least one day off a week, and for several days before an important event concentrate only on very light work. With experience, you will come to know when and how to move towards your peak.

Programme phases

Your programme should follow a basic format with these main phases:

Foundation	(4 to 8 weeks) The concentration in this phase is on basic fitness, building up aerobic endurance and strength, with a little muscular endurance work. This is the time to concentrate on any specific weaknesses in strength or movement.
Preparation	(9 to 12 weeks) Continue working on improving aerobic endurance, but move the emphasis to anaerobic endurance, i.e. shuttle running with some circuits and gym work to build muscular endurance.
Early competition endurance	(13 to 16 weeks) Maintain aerobic, anaerobic and muscular endurance training with some running, shuttles and circuits. The emphasis now moves to speed and movement.
Main competition	(17 to 20 weeks) Maintenance of all fitness elements. The emphasis is now on speed before important events with appropriate rests.

20 Week Build-Up Programme					
Week	Aerobic endurance	Anaerobic endurance	Strength	Circuit training	Speed	Flexibility
1	3		2	1		2
2	3		2	1		2
3	3		2	1		2
4	4		2	1		2
5	4		1	1		2
6	4		1	1		2
7	3	1	1	1		2
8	3	1	1	1		2
9	2	2	1	1		2
10	2	2	1	1		2
11	2	3	1	1		2
12	2	3	1	1		2
13	1	2	1	1	2	2
14	1	2	1	1	2	2
15	1	2	1	1	2	2
16	1	2	1	1	2	2
17	1	2	1		1	2
18	1	2	1		1	2
19	1	2	1		1	2
20	1	2	1		1	2

Select activities

Use the training section to select activities for each category within this programme.

Initially, test each activity and then progress it. Activities should be put together into training sessions.

CHAPTER SIX

INJURY PREVENTION

Playing and training for squash should increase your general and physical well-being but, as in most physical activities, there are dangers. Players taking up squash in middle age or after a long absence from strenuous exercise are advised to seek a medical check-up. Start playing or training gradually and build up your level of fitness with jogging or swimming. Don't attempt to train or play squash if you are unwell or have a viral infection.

Injuries in squash can result from traumatic incidents or from over-use. The former include accidents, such as being hit with the racket or ball; falls; the pulling of muscles or tendons; and the twisting of joints. The latter, like tennis elbow, come gradually and involve niggling pains which don't go away when you play. Many injuries can be prevented and, as the old saying goes, 'prevention is better than cure'.

Prevention

Becoming fit for squash is the best way to avoid injuries, but you don't want the training to be counterproductive. The importance of warming-up, cooling-down and stretching every time you play cannot be over-emphasized. A sudden stop in training can be one of the causes of muscle soreness and cramps. Cool down gradually after playing and training as this helps prevent stiffness – a potential cause of muscle strains and over-use injuries.

Over-training by young performers and especially over-concentration on physical training for competition can cause injuries, plus other physical and mental problems which may cause children to drop out of the sport. High-level adult training programmes should never be applied to growing children.

Shoes used for training should be appropriate to the task and surface. For example, squash shoes, which are thin soled, are not suitable for a running programme. Ideally, indoor running should be undertaken on a sprung surface.

First aid

Management of bruise, muscle, tendon and ligament injuries is carried out by the RICE treatment, which is designed to stop continuing bleeding in the damaged tissue and to aid early recovery.

R – **rest** the injured part for 24-72 hours, after which movement within the limits of pain may be started.

I – apply **ice** using ice packs or ice wrapped in a damp flannel. The ice should stay on for 5-15 minutes until the skin turns red.

C – **compression** bandaging should be applied with tubular or crepe bandages.

E – **elevation** limits swelling. Continue for up to 24 hours.

Injuries

Blisters These are caused by friction, often associated with new shoes, wrinkled socks, inappropriate footwear, hot courts and worn or thin insoles. Wear in new footwear gradually and use vaseline on any friction areas.

Heel bruising This can occur through repeated jarring and is a particular problem in squash. Use shock-absorbing pads and treat with daily rubbing of ice plus hot and cold dips.

Ankle sprains Follow the RICE treatment, and bandage from toe to knee using a tubular elastic bandage.

Muscle injuries Muscle tears and pulls must be treated with RICE. Rest for 48 hours. The early appearance of bruising in the skin suggests that the torn muscle will recover quickly and gentle stretching can start.

Knee injuries Don't play through pain in the knees. Rest and seek professional advice.

No matter how fit you are the danger of injury is ever present. Melissa Fryer receives attention for a knee injury suffered during a match.

Shoulder injuries Over-use shoulder injuries start as niggling pains which get worse. Rest from playing while the shoulder is painful and seek treatment.

Tennis elbow This is a common over-use problem. For pain on the outside of the elbow, rest a few days, treat with ice packs, soluble aspirin and a supporting bandage for the muscles of the forearm.

Rehabilitation

Don't try to play through pain and do try to understand the cause of an injury so that you can prevent it from happening again. Rehabilitation from injury can be a frustrating business, but players must adjust to the need for rest until the injury heals. Playing too soon can lead to further injuries and imbalances. Remedial exercise can aid recovery and these will often be given by a specialist physiotherapist.

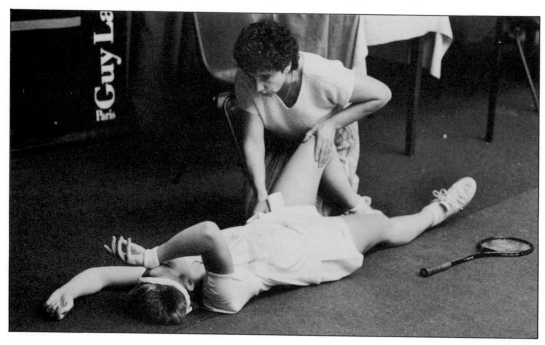

CHAPTER SEVEN

NUTRITION

Your diet provides the fuel on which you operate. If you get it wrong it can hinder your performance. For the competitive squash player in training, sensible eating provides energy at the right time. It is also important that a diet is balanced so that there are no deficiencies; that there is enough fuel provided to the muscles to match the speed with which it is being used and that refuelling of depleted energy reserves takes place.

A balanced diet requires carbohydrates and fats for fuel, and needs protein, minerals, vitamins and dietary fibre.

Carbohydrates, i.e. both starches and sugars, are the principal supply of energy. The carbohydrates recommended for the modern athlete are those that are found in natural unrefined food – the complex carbohydrates. These include bread and crispbreads made from wholemeal flour; wholewheat pasta; brown rice; peas, lentils, beans (kidney, haricot, baked etc.); pearl barley; sweetcorn, potatoes and root vegetables; breakfast cereals (Weetabix, Shredded Wheat, Bran Flakes, Puffed Wheat, porridge, sugar-free muesli); nuts; fresh fruit, dried fruit and canned fruits in natural juice.

Protein is also important for the squash player, especially for building muscle. Good sources of protein are meat, chicken, fish, eggs, milk, cheese, yoghurt, beans, lentils, wholewheat cereals, brown rice.

Diet recommendations

1 Consistent attention to nutrition is important, rather than attention in bursts.
2 You need a good balance of food to supply fuel for training and maintain stores of energy within the muscles.
3 Plan and organize your eating when training. Adapt your three meals a day habit to the demands of your training schedule.
4 During rest days, refuel with carbohydrates to make up for previous hurried eating.
5 Eat more low-energy food (vegetables, potatoes, fruit, cereals, nuts, beans and pulses; more wholemeal bread; emphasize complex carbohydrates *not* sweets and sugars, and try to reduce any fats in your diet.
6 Don't eat in the two hours before training, but allow time for food to leave the stomach. For high-fat foods this takes two to four hours, and for carbohydrates between one and two hours.
7 Take adequate fluid before training (up to 300ml/½ pint of water). Always replace fluids after a match or training.
8 Refuel between sessions. This is best done immediately after exercise.

CONCLUSION

'If only' you were fit enough to run down the last ball, to keep chasing through the longest game and hardest rallies, strong enough to bend, twist and bounce back to the T. 'If only' when you are both tired, you were able to increase the pressure on your tiring opponent, speed on to the loose ball and stretch to the ones that fly tantalizingly out of reach.

Fitness for squash does not have to be just a matter of hopes. You can improve your game by motivating and organizing yourself to use the activities in this book.

You cannot do everything, but you can assess your own individual needs, select accordingly from the activities outlined and use them to develop your fitness. Devise a training programme for both off and in seasons. If you have never had a programme before, you should work out a balanced and progressive programme that will fit in with your lifestyle, your commitments, and your training aims.

You *can* get better at squash and lift your game if you work at it. Get fit for the game and then get fitter to improve it.

Index

Numerals in *italics* refer to illustrations.